First Workshop on NLP in Agriculture and Livestock Management

New Delhi, India
15 December 2022

ISBN: 978-1-7138-9119-2

Printed from e-media with permission by:

Curran Associates, Inc.
57 Morehouse Lane
Red Hook, NY 12571

Association for Computational Linguistics
209 N. Eighth Street
Stroudsburg, Pennsylvania 18360

Phone: 1-570-476-8006
Fax: 1-570-476-0860

acl@aclweb.org

Additional copies of this publication are available from:

Curran Associates, Inc.
57 Morehouse Lane
Red Hook, NY 12571 USA
Phone: 845-758-0400
Fax: 845-758-2633
Email: curran@proceedings.com
Web: www.proceedings.com

2022

First Workshop on NLP in Agriculture and Livestock Management

Proceedings of the Workshop

December 15, 2022

Introduction

Currently, agriculture and livestock management are at a crossroads. There has been an increase in the world's population, a reduction in available farmland as well as competition for agricultural land from biofuels. Advances from traditional agricultural areas have been resisted by consumers and politicians, and consequently increases in productivity need to come from non-traditional areas to ensure that the world's population has access to basic nutrition at an affordable price. The Semantic and Natural Language Processing (NLP) community can assist the agricultural domain by providing unique insights from data or by providing greater clarity to current agricultural processes.

Agricultural and livestock researchers, in common with other domains, have access to large collections of documents such as scientific papers, news, social media data, etc. These textual documents can be analyzed and processed with NLP methods, supported by semantic knowledge, to resolve issues in digital agriculture and livestock management.

To date, the application of text mining and semantics in the agricultural domain remains underexplored. This Research Topic invites original research, surveys, and position papers that address issues in Agricultural Text Mining or Agri Semantics, in order to increase the visibility and application potential of this important and emerging research area.

Organizing Committee

Workshop Organizers

Manjira Sinha, IIT Kharagpur, India
Tirthankar Dasgupta, TCS Research, India
Sanjay Chatterjee, IIIT Kalyani, India

Program Committee

Program Committee

Manjira Sinha, IIT Kharagpur, India
Tirthankar Dasgupta, TCS Research, India
Sanjay Chatterjee, IIIT Kalyani, India
Adway Mitra, IIT Kharagpur, India

Table of Contents

Rice Cultivation in India – Challenges and Environmental Effects

Ushasi Bhattacharya

Department of Education
M V J College of Education
Bangalore, Karnataka, India, 560037
ushasibhattacharya1988@gmail.com

Abstract

Rice is one of the most cultivated grain crops in India as well as in Asian countries. It is a staple food in India. India is the second largest producer of Rice next to China. This crop is grown mainly in tropical and rain fed areas. In this paper, major types of Rice crops cultivated in India, the major challenges of cultivating Rice in India and its adverse effect in the environment are discussed. We have also discussed how the Computer Vision, Natural Language Processing, Mobile Applications and other technologies and research works can help to overcome these issues.

Keywords – Challenges of Rice Cultivation, Environmental Effect of Rice Cultivation, CV and NLP in Rice Cultivation.

1 Introduction

Rice is one of the most cultivated grain crops in India as well as in Asian countries. India ranks in the second position next to China in the cultivation and consumption of Rice. Rice grain belongs to the grass family of Graminae. It is cultivated in Rabi and Kharif seasons. In some parts of India Rice is cultivated three times in a year. Nutritional benefits of Rice include:

A. Good source of energy
B. Good source of Vitamin D, Calcium, Fiber, Iron, Thiamine, Carbohydrate, etc.
C. Cholesterol free
D. Helps in Blood pressure management
E. Prevents skin disease and chronic constipation
F. Rice Brand Oil support Cardio Vascular health

Major Rice production states in India are Indo-Gangetic and other River side states like West Bengal, Uttar Pradesh, Bihar, Punjab, Haryana, Odisha, Chhattisgarh, Andhra Pradesh, Telangana, Tamil Nadu, Kerala, Assam, etc. Punjab has made excellent prosperity in Rice cultivation during the last 60 years since the Green revolution began in 1960's in India. Punjab and Chhattisgarh are the Rice Bowl of India [Chanana (2001)].

Generally, Rice crop requires hot and humid weather, plentiful water supply and abundant sunshine. Ideal temperature ranges from $20^{O}C$ to $40^{O}C$ and ideal rainfall ranges from 100 CM to 200 CM. Traditionally, Rice farming requires about 6 inches clogged water for rice transplantation. Rice can be grown on a wide variety of soils such as silts, loams, gravels, acidic as well as alkaline soil, soil with low permeability and PH varying from 5.0 to 9.5. Deep fertile i.e., reach in organic matters clayey or loamy soils with low permeability, free of water logging and sodicity are considered best for Rice cultivation. Major varieties of Rice cultivated in India, their maturity time and average yield production are shown in Table 1.

2 Related Works

Dwivedy (2011) has discussed some challenges faced by the Indian agricultural sector such as illiteracy, poor socio-economic background, unawareness of modern technology and equipment, small and fragmented land holdings, natural calamities, etc. Mehta (2014) analyses how agricultural mechanizations and power operated farm equipment play a vital role in progressing cultivation productivity in developing countries over the traditional human and animal power operated equipment. Mandala (2021) focuses on unavailability of proper market and financial problems encountered by the farmers. Dhakshana (2018) criticises the obstacles encountered by the farmers to get the agricultural loans provided by the Govt. banks to buy farm equipment.

Proceedings of the Workshop on NLP in Agriculture and Livestock Management, pages 1 - 4
December 15, 2022 ©2022 Association for Computational Linguistics

Variety Name	Average Maturity Period	Average Paddy Yield
PR 128	111 Days	30.5 Quintals/Acre
PR 129	108 Days	30 Quintals/Acre
HKR 47	104 Days	29.5 Quintals/Acre
PR 111	135 Days	27 Quintals/Acre
PR 113	142 Days	28 Quintals/Acre
PR 114	145 Days	27.5 Quintals/Acre
PR 115	125 Days	25 Quintals/Acre
PR 116	144 Days	28 Quintals/Acre
PR 118	158 Days	29 Quintals/Acre
PR 120	132 Days	28.5 Quintals/Acre
PR 121	140 Days	30.5 Quintals/Acre
PR 122	147 Days	31.5 Quintals/Acre
PR 123	143 Days	29 Quintals/Acre
PR 126	123 Days	30 Quintals/Acre
PR 127	137 Days	30 Quintals/Acre
CSR 30	142 Days	13.5 Quintals/Acre
Punjab Basmati 3	139 Days	16 Quintals/Acre
Punjab Basmati 4	146 Days	17 Quintals/Acre
Punjab Basmati 5	137 Days	15 Quintals/Acre
Pusa Punjab Basmati 1509	120 Days	15.7 Quintals/Acre
Pusa Basmati 1121	137 Days	13.7 Quintals/Acre
Pusa 44	145 Days	6 Quintals/Acre
Pusa Basmati 1637	138 Days	17.5 Quintals/Acre
Hybrid 6201	125 Days	25 Quintals/Acre
Vivek Dhan 62	125 Days	19 Quintals/Acre
Karnataka Rice Hybrid 2	125 Days	35 Quintals/Acre
Ratnagiri 1	115 Days	19 Quintals/Acre
Ratnagiri 2	145 Days	21 Quintals/Acre

Table 1: Major Rice Varieties Cultivated in India

Zaveri (2016) points out how ground water overuse leads to threatening decrease in ground water resources which in turn results in declining agricultural production. This also has drastic effects on climate change. Gandhi (1999) examine the role of agroindustries in India in the context of rural and small farmers' development.

Dhakshana (2017) focuses on a number of challenging factors of direct marketing faced by the farmers. The scarcity of cold storage results in heavy competition and makes direct marketing even more complicated. Azam (2019) explores the challenges of marketing faced by the conventional and organic farmers such as inadequate storage, unawareness of market price, inequality between demand and supply of crop, transportation problem, price variation in different markets, lack of Govt. support, etc.

Patel and Patel (2016) analyses how android apps of agricultural serviced influence the Indian farmers in their crop cultivation. Mahapatra (2020) provides views of how smartphone apps work as an important tool for agricultural information during the Covid'19 lockdown period in India.

3 Challenges Faced by the Rice Farmers in India

Being a third world country majority of population belongs to the rural India. Here, agriculture is the livelihood of most of the rural people. Although Rice is a staple food crop of India, Rice cultivation is not a profitable job for Indian farmers. In this section, we point out some of the major challenges encountered by the Rice farmers.

A. Poor Economic condition of Farmers

Agriculture is the primary livelihood of majority of the Indian rural people. 80% farmers are marginal and small in yield production. They work 80 hours per week along with their family members to earn their livelihood. They often take loans from money lenders at high interest for buying seed, machine, fertilizer, insecticide, pesticide, and so on. The interest paid to the money lenders is always higher than the interest taken by the loans provided by the Govt. organizations. But due to unavailability or unawareness of the Govt. initiatives they go for these high interest payers. These causes severe impact on farmers including suicide.

B. Unavailability of Good Quality of Seeds

As the good quality seeds are expensive and have scarcity in the market poor and marginal farmers can not afford them. Most of the seed manufacturers are private companies. Poor farmers have no other options than to buy poor quality seeds which are less productive.

C. Lack of modern Equipment and Technology

Due to the lack of awareness of the modern technology majority of India farmers do not use modern agricultural equipment. They highly depend on traditional tools like bullock drawn plough, sickle, etc. It takes more energy, manpower and labour cost. In return it provides less profit.

Rich farmers use machines in irrigation, harvesting and transportation. But these machines are dependent on continuous power supply.

D. Poor Irrigation Facility

Paddy cultivation needs high quantity of water. The regions having 100-200 CM average rainfall are suitable for Rice cultivation. Many regions of India lacks the required rainfall. So the farmers depend on irrigation facilities essential for growing crops. India has the second largest irrigated land next to USA. But only one third of the irrigated land has proper irrigation facility. Punjab has about 98% irrigated land because of abundance of water from the snow melt rivers and dams throughout the year. But the condition of the other parts of India is quite different. In central India rivers are rain felt. They don't carry water throughout the year. So, in this region farmers have to wait for the monsoon which is uncertain.

E. Small and Fragmented Land

The size of farming land per farmer is decreasing every year. This is due to the system of inheritance law of India. For example, a person having 4 children each having 2 children when dies his land is distributed in 4 parts which in turn is divided into 8 parts. Due to this system, most of the farmers have small amount of fragmented lands. Small portion of land has more irrigation problems because the irrigated water often flows to surrounding fields.

F. Absence of Proper market

Often farmers do not get reasonable selling price of their crops. This happens due to the unavailability of proper market and lack of storage facility. Farmers sell crops to middlemen at a lower price which is sold to market at higher price. Thus the impact of market price does not reach to the end farmers.

G. Transportation Problem

Transportation is a major problem in Indian agriculture. There are many villages which are not properly connected to city. Many roads are either broken or narrow. During and after the monsoon these roads become muddy. That time the transportation is at stalemate. The transportation between two places which are separated by water is more challenging.

4 Adverse Effects of Rice Cultivation upon Environment

Here, we discuss some adverse effects of Rice cultivation in our environment.

A. Emission of Green House Gasses

Rice is often grown in flooded areas. Rice fields needs to be submerged in waters. These clogged water generated greenhouse gasses such as Carbon Dioxide, Methane, Nitrogen Oxide, Nitrogen Dioxide, Nitrous Oxide, etc. Release of these greenhouse gasses increase global warming.

B. Climate Change

After the cultivation Rice is stored into granary. The straws and husks are left out. Farmers often burn these left out straws and husks in the field. This emits Carbon Dioxide and other greenhouse gasses and causes global warming. It also causes soil depletion and soil pollution.

C. Spread of Mosquitos and Other Insects and Bacteria

As Rice requires much water, the clogged water produces mosquitos, other insects and bacteria. This is due to the fact that stagnant water is the ideal place giving birth of mosquito Larva. These causes spread of malaria, dengue, other life threatening diseases.

D. Misuse of Water Resources

Rice cultivation needs average 100 to 200 CM rainfall. It is highly water consuming crop. Most of the time because of poor irrigation system and delayed monsoon a large amount of underground water is used Rice cultivation. Deep tube wells are used for drawing underground water. These deep tube wells need high electricity consumption. A great amount of water resources is wasted in this way.

5 MS Word STREAM Tools

Usage of technologies in agricultural sector has replaced human efforts. Farming functions such as use of machinery, use of fertilizers and production of raw products have been successfully automated. Some of such technologies and their appropriate usage in Rice cultivation are discussed here.

A large number of Android apps provide latest market price, weather prediction, Govt. policies and skims for farmers, latest technologies, videos, and news related to agriculture. They have used Computer Vision and Natural Language Processing research works for different tasks. The functionalities of some of these apps are mentioned below.

Agri App: It is an online farming platform which provides Chat interface between farmers and experts. This app includes video messages for farmers.

Iffco Kisan App: It provides latest information, latest market price, various farming tips, weather forecast in 10 different Indian languages.

Agri Media Video App: It is an online marketplace. It provides chat service for farmers with the option of uploading images of crops.

Farm Bee RML Farmer: This app available in 10 Indian languages provides informative agriculture content at every stage of the crop life cycle. It provides market price and weather forecast based on a user location. Farmers can choose from 450 crop varieties and 1300 markets.

Kisan Yojana: It provides information about Govt. schemes to farmer (Kisan).

Pusa Krishi: It is launched by Ministry of Agriculture and Farmers welfare, Govt. of India in 2016. It provides information on crop varieties developed by ICAR and latest technology developed by IARI.

6 Conclusion

Insufficient soil moisture, poor soil fertility, soil erosion, draught, flood, flash flood, water logging, uncertain monsoon, and inefficient use of fertilizer are major challenges in Rice cultivation. Rice cultivation adversely effects in climate change. In turn, Rice cultivation itself is affected by the climate change by reducing production. In this paper, we have analyzed the challenges faced by the Indian farmers and the adverse effects of overall Rice cultivation. This will help the farmers to get aware of the issues regarding Rice cultivation. We have also provided some important aspects of technologies and research works which may benefit the farmers if they use them intensively.

References

Ashwani Chanana, *"Economic Condition of Farmers in India" Mobile Robots, vol. 8, no. 2, pp. 520-531, March 2001.*

Dwivedy, Nidhi. *"Challenges faced by the agriculture sector in developing countries with special reference to India." International journal of rural studies 18.2 (2011).*

Mehta, C. R., N. S. Chandel, and Thangavelu Senthilkumar. *"Status, challenges and strategies for farm mechanization in India." Agricultural Mechanization in Asia, Africa and Latin America 45.4 (2014): 43-50.*

Mandala, Gangu Naidu, Pallawi Baldeo Sangode, S. Anjani Devi, and Venkata Ramakrishna Rao Gandreti. *"Problems and Constraints Faced by Farmers in Financing and Marketing of Agricultural Produce in India."* Universal Journal of Accounting and Finance 9, no. 2 (2021): 139-144.

Dhakshana, Aarthi, and K. V. R. Rajandran. *"Challenges and problems on farmers' access to agricultural credit facilities in Cauvery Delta, Thanjavur District." St. Theresa Journal of Humanities and Social Sciences 4.1 (2018): 50-62.*

Zaveri, Esha, Danielle S. Grogan, Karen Fisher-Vanden, Steve Frolking, Richard B. Lammers, Douglas H. Wrenn, Alexander Prusevich, and Robert E. Nicholas. *"Invisible water, visible impact: groundwater use and Indian agriculture under climate change." Environmental Research Letters 11, no. 8 (2016): 084005.*

Gandhi, Vasant, Gauri Kumar, and Robin Marsh. *"Agroindustry for rural and small farmer development: issues and lessons from India." The International Food and Agribusiness Management Review 2.3-4 (1999): 331-344.*

Dhakshana, J. A., and K. V. R. Rajandran. *"A study on challenges faced by the farmers in direct marketing, the rural business series." Indian Journal of science and research 14.1 (2017): 91-97.*

Azam, Md Sikandar, Musarrat Shaheen, and Sonali Narbariya. *"Marketing challenges and organic farming in India—Does farm size matter?." International Journal of Nonprofit and Voluntary Sector Marketing 24.4 (2019): e1654.*

Patel, Hetal, and Dharmendra Patel. *"Survey of android apps for agriculture sector." International Journal of Information Sciences and Techniques 6.1-2 (2016): 61-67.*

A custom CNN model for detection of rice disease under complex environment

Chiranjit Pal
Computer Science & Engineering
Indian Institute of Information Technology
Kalyani, India
chiranjit_jrf21@iiitkalyani.ac.in

Sanjoy Pratihar
Computer Science & Engineering
Indian Institute of Information Technology
Kalyani, India
sanjoy@iiitkalyani.ac.in

Imon Mukherjee
Computer Science & Engineering
Indian Institute of Information Technology
Kalyani, India
imon@iiitkalyani.ac.in

***Abstract*—The work in this paper designs an image-based rice disease detection framework that takes rice plant image as input and identifies the presence of BrownSpot disease in the image fed into the system. A CNN-based disease detection scheme performs the binary classification task on our custom dataset containing 2223 images of healthy and unhealthy classes under complex environments. Experimental results show that our system is able to achieve consistently satisfactory results in performing disease detection tasks. Furthermore, the CNN disease detection model compares with state-of-the-art works and procures an accuracy of 96.8%.**

***Index Terms*—Rice disease, CNN model, Crop segmentation, Image processing**

I. Introduction

FOr identifying or categorizing diseases in plant images, a number of traditional machine learning-based approaches have been cited [Guo et al.(2020)Guo, Zhang, Yin, Hu, Zou, Xue, and Wang] that include support vector machine (SVM) [Jiang et al.(2020)Jiang, Lu, Chen, Cai, and Li], Artificial Neural Network (ANN) [Orillo et al.(2014)Orillo, Cruz, Agapito, Satimbre, and Valenzuela], and so one. The drawback of those approaches is that they require manual hand-crafted features. Recently, the Deep learning approach, particularly Convolution Neural Networks (CNN), eliminated this problem by automatically learning the relevant features needed to classify or detect the objects of interest. For example, a novel automatic rice disease detection approach based on CNN model is introduced in [Liang et al.(2019)Liang, Zhang, Zhang, and Cao]. This model presents a comparison and accuracy analysis between traditional low-level features produced by local binary pattern histograms (LBPH) and Haar-WT with high-level features produced by the CNN model. The system realizes two classifier models; CNN merged with Softmax and CNN merged with SVM. The former model with high-level features shows higher accuracy than the latter.

This research work is designed and developed as part of project work sponsored by the Ministry of Electronics and Information Technology (MeitY), Govt. of India.

Another work on an automatic wheat disease detection system based on four different CNN models has been presented in [Lu et al.(2017a)Lu, Hu, Zhao, Mei, and Zhang]. The method takes 50,000 pictures of unhealthy and healthy wheat crops into consideration. Among the four types of model, VGG-16 model provides the maximum average accuracy of 97.95%. The models in [Liang et al.(2019)Liang, Zhang, Zhang, and Cao] and [Lu et al.(2017a)Lu, Hu, Zhao, Mei, and Zhang] perform the task of disease detection by increasing the processing speed and robustness of the system at work. However, these models can detect only a limited number of diseases of the paddy plant. The model [Lu et al.(2017b)Lu, Yi, Zeng, Liu, and Zhang] overcomes this issue by increasing the number of recognizable diseases to ten. To train the model inspired by Alexnet and LeNet-5, 500 images are used. Although the experimental results have attained an average detection accuracy of 95.48%, the number of images for ten classes is very small when considering the deep learning model. The work in [Aukkapinyo et al.(2020)Aukkapinyo, Sawangwong, Pooyoi, and Kusakunniran] presents another system model called Stack CNN on the detection of the infected area of rice plants and pests. The work finds six different diseases: Neck Blast, Sheath Rot, Brown Spot, Bacterial Leaf Blight, False Smut, Sheath and, Blight, and three pest varieties: Stem Borer, Hispa, and Brown Plant Hopper. The novelty of the study lies in its ease and applicability. Methods in [Liang et al.(2019)Liang, Zhang, Zhang, and Cao], [Lu et al.(2017a)Lu, Hu, Zhao, Mei, and Zhang], and [Lu et al.(2017b)Lu, Yi, Zeng, Liu, and Zhang] could only accept paddy leaf images for disease classification. However, the model can identify plant disease in any portion of the rice plant. Moreover, it can correctly predict the disease when it infects the non-leaf parts of the plant body. The study also recognizes five existing CNN models and compares their performance with the help of transfer learning and without learning. Out of the five models, the VGG16 outperforms in terms of accuracy. The stacked CNN is able to classify the

Proceedings of the Workshop on NLP in Agriculture and Livestock Management, pages 5 - 8
December 15, 2022 ©2022 Association for Computational Linguistics

diseases and pests with 95% accuracy.

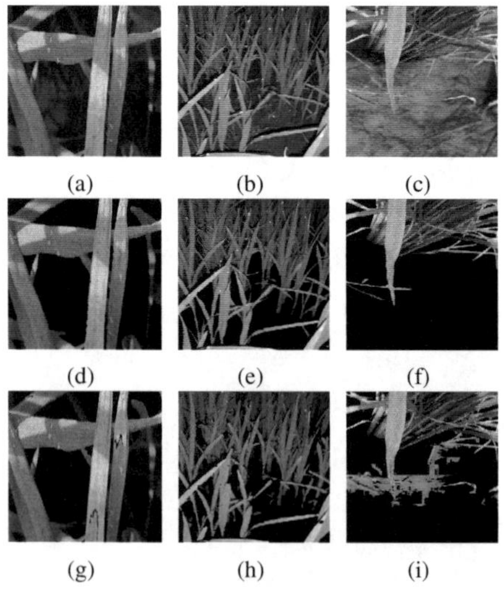

Fig. 1: Visual-based description of the paddy field dataset: Fig. (a)-(c) depict the images under various background conditions; (a) Shadows image on an unclouded day; (b) The scene of the crop field taken in the evening time; (c) Soil and disease color near to each other; Fig. (d)-(f) present the images done by manual segmentation; Fig. (g)-(i) depict output images by the automated segmentation approach.

The current work has the following contributions:

1) A custom dataset of 2223 rice plant images is taken directly from the rice field using an ordinary mobile handset camera.
2) A custom CNN architecture is designed to distinguish between healthy and unhealthy rice plants. Experimental results show that the crop segmentation technique enhances the performance of the CNN model by extracting only the regions of interest parts from the images of the given custom dataset.

II. Materials and Methods

A. Data Acquisition

A total of 2223 RGB images containing healthy and BrowSpot disease are captured from the paddy field in Durgapur, West Bengal under different lighting conditions. We have considered RGB images that are captured during the early and middle harvesting season as presented in Fig. 1. The description of the dataset is presented in Table I.

TABLE I: Dataset split description

Name of the Class	Train	Test
Diseased	1000	400
Healthy	556	267

B. Data Pre-processing

To remove the unwanted part from the image, we have applied a crop segmentation approach [Pal et al.(2022)Pal, Pratihar, Chatterji, and Mukherjee] in the current work such that it becomes easy for the classifier to identify the diseased portions in the image. Furthermore, the crop extraction algorithm uses the features from the edges of the object of interest parts and color indices of an image to segregate the plant part from the background of the image. The resultant image produced by the crop segmentation approach consists of plant parts (both diseased and healthy), as shown in Fig. 1. These processed images will be used to process the disease detection model further.

C. Custom CNN Model

The CNN model has gained so much popularity in the computer vision domain [Sharma et al.(2020)Sharma, Berwal, and Ghai], [Koklu et al.(2021)Koklu, Cinar, and Taspinar]. For this reason, we have deployed a custom CNN model for our problem. In the proposed CNN model binary cross entropy function is deployed as the work is defined for the two-class classification problem. The system is designed using three convolution layers and two Max- pooling layers. Each of the intermediate layers is attached to the ReLU activation function, and the last layer, called the output layer, is attached to Softmax as an activation function. For parameter adjustment, the learning rate is fixed at 0.001. The epochs are set to 10. The weight decay for the model is 0.0001, and the train batch size is 32. The detailed architecture of the custom CNN model is demonstrated in Fig.2.

D. Pretrained CNN Models

The ResNet50 [Qiang et al.(2019)Qiang, He, and Dai] and Inception V3 [Chen et al.(2020)Chen, Chen, Zhang, Sun, and Nanehkaran] are applied in the experiment, which detects paddy leaf diseases from the custom dataset. The considered models: ResNet50 and Inception V3 comprise of 50 and 48 layers, respectively. The ResNet50 is trained with 23 million trainable parameters. The model consists of five stages of convolution and identity blocks, whereas the architecture of Inception V3 is inherited from the Inception family. It is the modified version as it includes Factorized 7×7 convolutions, label Smoothing, and the application of a secondary classifier to forward class information downward the network.

III. Result and Analysis

A. Experiments on Classifiers using Custom Dataset:

In our experimental setup, a custom dataset of 2223 images is split into two parts; one part contains 1556 training images and another part contains 667 testing images. To verify the model's validity, test images unknown to the model are applied to it. In many cases model suffers from the over fitting problem. To overcome this over fitting problem, a data augmentation technique has been deployed. Data augmentation includes rotation, translation, flipping, cropping, and scaling. The model has gained an accuracy of 98.6% during the training phase and

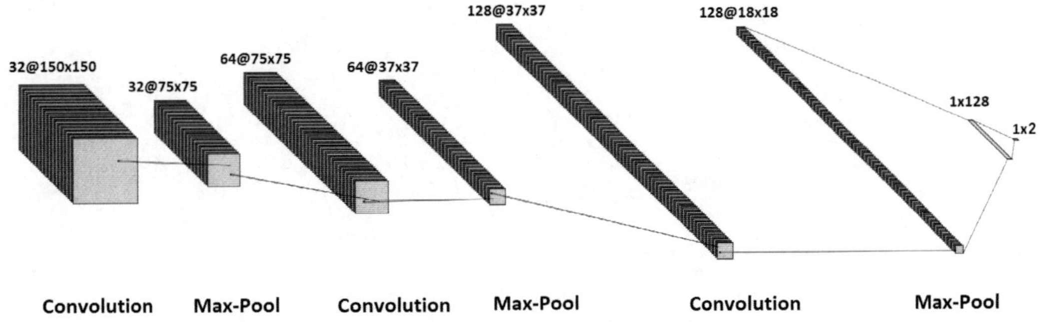

Fig. 2: Architecture of the proposed CNN model.

TABLE II: Accuracy and loss of considered models with 10 epochs.The models are deployed on images without segmentation

Model Name	Train Accuracy	Train Loss	Test Accuracy	Test Loss
ResNet50	0.961	0.125	0.875	0.400
Inception V3	0.976	0.233	0.928	0.238
Proposed CNN	0.960	0.130	0.928	0.182

TABLE III: Accuracy and loss of considered models with 10 epochs.The models are deployed on images with segmentation

Model Name	Train Accuracy	Train Loss	Test Accuracy	Test Loss
ResNet50	0.988	0.034	0.973	0.039
Inception V3	0.993	0.159	0.989	0.162
Proposed CNN	0.986	0.014	0.968	0.136

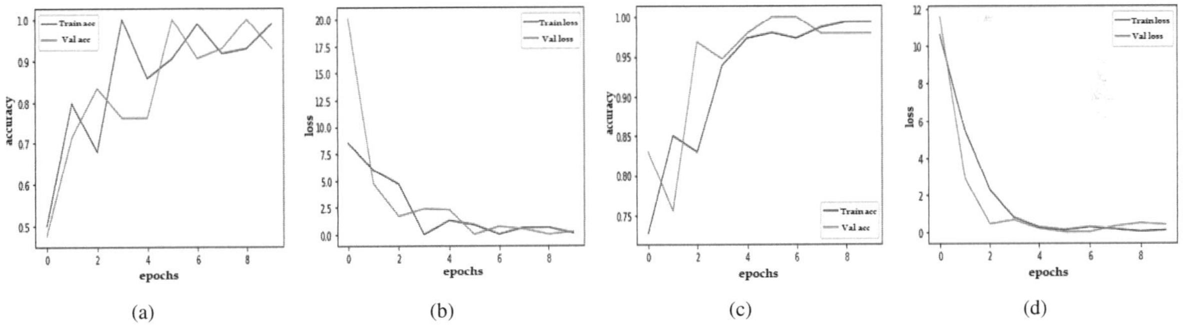

Fig. 3: Inception V3 model performance metrics after 10 epochs; (a) and (b) depict accuracy and loss of the considered model without segmentation; (c) and (d) represent the accuracy and loss of the considered model with segmentation.

96.8% accuracy during the testing phase on the custom dataset without segmentation. To compare the accomplishment of the proposed model, the same dataset is applied to other state-of-the-art works. Table III and Table II show that the proposed model has provided consistent accuracy during the training and testing images. To ensure that the crop segmentation will help in enhancing the performance of disease recognizer models, the processed images are passed to Inception V3, Resnet50, and our proposed model. Table III shows that the accuracy of the model is increased with the segmented images. Hence, the experimental outcomes conclude that the proposed CNN model can enhance the accuracy when combined with the image segmentation approach. The pictorial representations of accuracy and loss curves of Inception V3, custom CNN, and Resnet50 are shown in Fig. 3, Fig. 4, and Fig. 5 respectively.

IV. Conclusion

The main task of the current work was to implement an automated BrownSpot disease detection system that works on images captured from the paddy field. The proposed model can detect the presence of BrownSpot disease in a rice plant

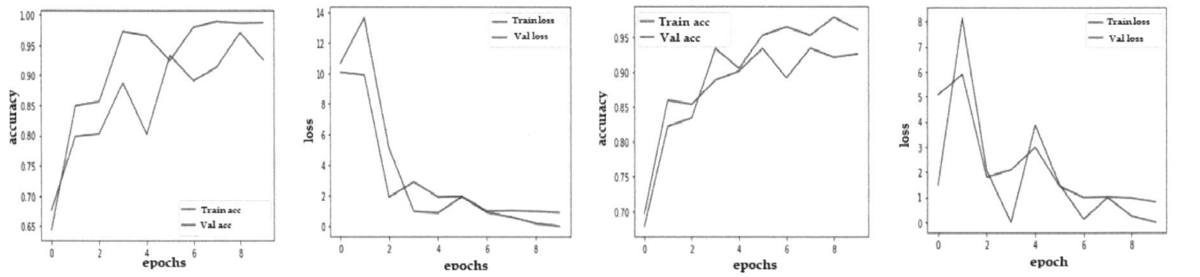

(a) (b) (c) (d)

Fig. 4: Proposed CNN model performance metrics after 10 epochs; (a) and (b) depict the accuracy and loss of the considered model with segmentation; (c) and (d) represent the accuracy and loss of the considered model without segmentation.

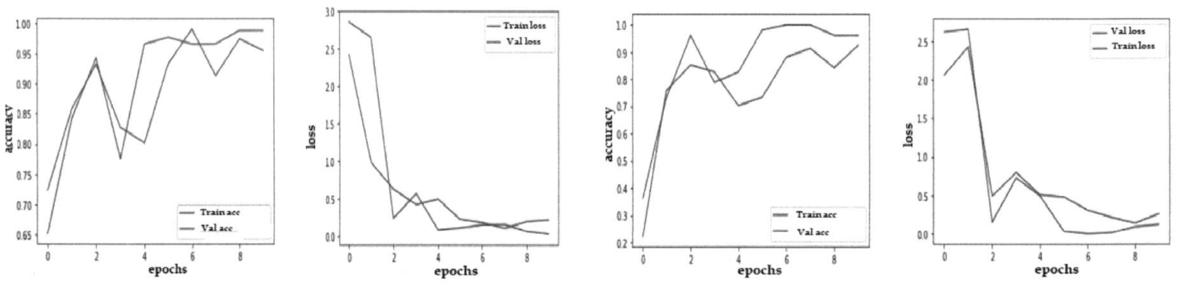

(a) (b) (c) (d)

Fig. 5: Resnet50 model performance metrics after 10 epochs: (a) and (b) depict the accuracy and loss of the considered model with segmentation; (c) and (d) represent the accuracy and loss of the considered model without segmentation.

leaf with reliable accuracy. In the future, we wish to build a mobile-based application that will help farmers to recognize the category and severity of rice disease without help of human expertise.

REFERENCES

[Aukkapinyo et al.(2020)Aukkapinyo, Sawangwong, Pooyoi, and Kusakunniran] Kittinun Aukkapinyo, Suchakree Sawangwong, Parintorn Pooyoi, and Worapan Kusakunniran. 2020. Localization and classification of rice-grain images using region proposals-based convolutional neural network. *International Journal of Automation and Computing*, 17(2):233–246.

[Chen et al.(2020)Chen, Chen, Zhang, Sun, and Nanehkaran] Junde Chen, Jinxiu Chen, Defu Zhang, Yuandong Sun, and Yaser Ahangari Nanehkaran. 2020. Using deep transfer learning for image-based plant disease identification. *Computers and Electronics in Agriculture*, 173:105393.

[Guo et al.(2020)Guo, Zhang, Yin, Hu, Zou, Xue, and Wang] Yan Guo, Jin Zhang, Chengxin Yin, Xiaonan Hu, Yu Zou, Zhipeng Xue, and Wei Wang. 2020. Plant disease identification based on deep learning algorithm in smart farming. *Discrete Dynamics in Nature and Society*, 2020.

[Jiang et al.(2020)Jiang, Lu, Chen, Cai, and Li] Feng Jiang, Yang Lu, Yu Chen, Di Cai, and Gongfa Li. 2020. Image recognition of four rice leaf diseases based on deep learning and support vector machine. *Computers and Electronics in Agriculture*, 179:105824.

[Koklu et al.(2021)Koklu, Cinar, and Taspinar] Murat Koklu, Ilkay Cinar, and Yavuz Selim Taspinar. 2021. Classification of rice varieties with deep learning methods. *Computers and Electronics in Agriculture*, 187:106285.

[Liang et al.(2019)Liang, Zhang, Zhang, and Cao] Wan-jie Liang, Hong Zhang, Gu-feng Zhang, and Hong-xin Cao. 2019. Rice blast disease recognition using a deep convolutional neural network. *Scientific Reports*, 9(1):1–10.

[Lu et al.(2017a)Lu, Hu, Zhao, Mei, and Zhang] Jiang Lu, Jie Hu, Guannan Zhao, Fenghua Mei, and Changshui Zhang. 2017a. An in-field automatic wheat disease diagnosis system. *Computers and Electronics in Agriculture*, 142:369–379.

[Lu et al.(2017b)Lu, Yi, Zeng, Liu, and Zhang] Yang Lu, Shujuan Yi, Nianyin Zeng, Yurong Liu, and Yong Zhang. 2017b. Identification of rice diseases using deep convolutional neural networks. *Neurocomputing*, 267:378–384.

[Orillo et al.(2014)Orillo, Cruz, Agapito, Satimbre, and Valenzuela] John William Orillo, Jennifer Dela Cruz, Leobelle Agapito, Paul Jensen Satimbre, and Ira Valenzuela. 2014. Identification of diseases in rice plant (oryza sativa) using back propagation artificial neural network. In *2014 International Conference on Humanoid, Nanotechnology, Information Technology, Communication and Control, Environment and Management (HNICEM)*, pages 1–6. IEEE.

[Pal et al.(2022)Pal, Pratihar, Chatterji, and Mukherjee] Chiranjit Pal, Sanjoy Pratihar, Sanjay Chatterji, and Imon Mukherjee. 2022. Automatic rice crop extraction using edge based color features and color indices. In *2022 2nd Asian Conference on Innovation in Technology (ASIANCON)*, pages 1–8. IEEE.

[Qiang et al.(2019)Qiang, He, and Dai] Zhenping Qiang, Libo He, and Fei Dai. 2019. Identification of plant leaf diseases based on inception v3 transfer learning and fine-tuning. In *International Conference on Smart City and Informatization*, pages 118–127. Springer.

[Sharma et al.(2020)Sharma, Berwal, and Ghai] Parul Sharma, Yash Paul Singh Berwal, and Wiqas Ghai. 2020. Performance analysis of deep learning cnn models for disease detection in plants using image segmentation. *Information Processing in Agriculture*, 7(4):566–574.

Author Index

NOTES

NOTES

NOTES

NOTES